Contents

M H Was

C000097110

Sequences

Sequences are made where numbers follow patterns.

They can be made in many different ways. Look at these number sequences:

3 , 5 , 7 , 9 , ...   In this one we are adding 2 to each previous number.
+2   +2   +2   So the next numbers in the sequence will be 11, 13 and so on.

24 , 20 , 16 , ...   In this one we are subtracting 4 from each previous number.
-4   -4   So the next number in the sequence will be 12.

3 , 5 , 8 , 12 , ...   In this one we are increasing the number added each time.
+2   +3   +4

3 , 6 , 12 , 24 , ...   Here we are multiplying the previous number by 2 each time.
x2   x2   x2

We can make sequences from dot patterns as well:

1   4   9

These square patterns give us the **square numbers**.
So the next number in this sequence is 16.

We can make triangle numbers from triangular patterns:

1   3   6   10 ...

Find the two missing numbers in each of the following sequences:

(a)   5, 11, 17, 23,   ,   , ...

(b)   55, 46, 37, 28,   ,   , ...

(c)   2, 3, 6, 11,   ,   , ...

(d)   128, 64, 32, 16,   ,   , ...

(e) $\frac{1}{3}$, 1, 3, 9 ,   ,   , ...

(f) $\frac{1}{2}, \frac{2}{3}, \frac{3}{4}, \frac{4}{5}$,   ,   , ...

(g)   1, 4, 9, 16,   ,   , ...

(h)   2, 3, 5, 9, 17,   ,   , ...

(i)   0, 2, 6,   , 20,   , 42, ...

(j)   1, 4, 3, 6, 5,   , 7, 10,   , ...

Addition and Decimals: Revision

To add numbers together it is helpful to put them into columns and to line up the units:

For example, if we would like to
add together 4316, 784, 16 and 2970
we should write the sum out like this:

It is **very** important that the digits are
in straight lines in the columns:

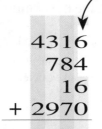

$$\begin{array}{r} 4316 \\ 784 \\ 16 \\ + \ 2970 \\ \hline \end{array}$$

$$\begin{array}{r} 4316 \\ 784 \\ 16 \\ + \ 2970 \\ \hline \end{array}$$

If you make sure that
the units digits are all
in line, it is easy to line
up the other digits.

On some rough paper, work out the answers to the following additions.
Do not use a calculator! Even though this is 'rough' work it must still be very tidy:

The digits must be in the correct columns.
The units must be lined up.

(a) $1642 + 318 + 76 =$

(b) $53 + 198 + 2417 + 862 =$

(c) $2999 + 769 + 5 + 1248 =$

(d) $128 + 67 + 5469 + 782 + 2413 =$

(e) $7 + 698 + 432 + 85 + 1784 =$

(f) $6419 + 802 + 380 + 57 =$

Adding decimal numbers together is just as easy.

For example, if we would like to
add together 6·7, 19·56, 4 and 316
we should write the sum out like this:

Some people find it easier to write
the sum out using noughts to fill up
all the gaps, like this:

$$\begin{array}{r} 6 \cdot 7 \\ 19 \cdot 56 \\ 4 \\ + \quad 316 \\ \hline \end{array}$$

Again we make sure
that the units digits
are all in line.

$$\begin{array}{r} 6 \cdot 70 \\ 19 \cdot 56 \\ 4 \cdot 00 \\ + \quad 316 \cdot 00 \\ \hline \end{array}$$

Whichever way you choose to write the question, don't forget to write the decimal point
in your answer and to keep the decimal points in line as well as the units.

On some rough paper, work out the answers to the following additions:

(g) $23 \cdot 7 + 4 \cdot 65 + 29 =$

(h) $6 \cdot 2 + 12 \cdot 48 + 186 + 1016 =$

(i) $3 \cdot 75 + 18 \cdot 28 + 8 \cdot 4 + 22 =$

(j) $300 + 30 \cdot 1 + 0 \cdot 33 + 3 \cdot 03 + 33 =$

Subtraction and Decimals: Revision

When subtracting it is important to remember several points:

1. Always start at the **top**, in the **right-hand column.**

2. When the figure at the top is too small we can **only** find extra by using some from the **next column**.

$$\begin{array}{r} 738 \\ -\ 196 \\ \hline 2 \end{array}$$

Here we have enough units because 8 subtract 6 is 2 ... but we need extra tens.

We can get extra tens by using one of the hundreds. Now we can say "13 tens subtract 9 tens is 4 tens; 6 hundreds subtract 1 hundred is 5 hundreds".

$$\begin{array}{r} ^6\!\!\not7^1\!\!38 \\ -\ 196 \\ \hline 542 \end{array}$$

3. Sometimes there are none available from the next higher column:

$$\begin{array}{r} 506 \\ -\ 178 \\ \hline \end{array}$$

Starting at the units we see that we have to subtract 8 but we only have 6. We can **only** get extra units by using a ten .... so our first job must be to get some extra tens by using one of the hundreds.

We now have 4 hundreds and 10 tens. We use one of these tens to make 10 extra units. We now have 16 units but only 9 tens:

$$\begin{array}{r} ^4\!\!\not5^9\!\not0^1\!6 \\ -\ 178 \\ \hline 328 \end{array}$$

On some rough paper, work out the following subtractions without using a calculator.

(a)	796 - 243 =	(b)	2714 - 387 =
(c)	3006 - 1597 =	(d)	12064 - 5988 =
(e)	214167 - 38908 =	(f)	8000 - 2419 =

When subtracting decimal numbers, don't forget to write the decimal point in your answer and to keep the decimal points in line as well as the units.

$$\begin{array}{r} 8\cdot6 \\ -\ 3\cdot25 \\ \hline \end{array}$$

This question is easier to do if you fill the gap in the hundredths column with a 0.

$$\begin{array}{r} 8\cdot6^5\!\not0 \\ -\ 3\cdot25 \\ \hline 5\cdot35 \end{array}$$

Look carefully at how to do questions such as 24 subtract 1·72:

$$\begin{array}{r} 2\not4^3\!\cdot\not0^1\!9\!\not0 \\ -\ 1\cdot72 \\ \hline 22\cdot28 \end{array}$$

On some rough paper, work out the answers to the following subtractions:

(g)	16·7 - 3·2 =	(h)	7·65 - 4·2 =	(i)	6·3 - 1·25 =
(j)	14 - 8·7 =	(k)	214·3 - 98·89 =	(l)	1000 - 1·7 =

Equivalent Fractions

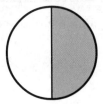 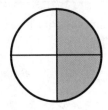 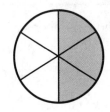

Each of these circles has the same amount shaded.

So $\quad \dfrac{1}{2} \quad = \quad \dfrac{2}{4} \quad = \quad \dfrac{3}{6}$

In these fractions the **denominator** (bottom number) is twice the **numerator** (top number).

(a) Fill in the missing numbers: $\quad \dfrac{1}{2} = \dfrac{2}{4} = \dfrac{3}{6} = \dfrac{\square}{8} = \dfrac{5}{\square} = \dfrac{\square}{\square}$

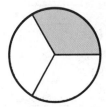 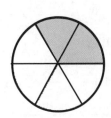 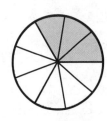

Each of these circles has the same amount shaded.

So $\quad \dfrac{1}{3} \quad = \quad \dfrac{2}{6} \quad = \quad \dfrac{3}{9}$

In these fractions the **denominator** is three times the **numerator**.

(b) Fill in the missing numbers: $\quad \dfrac{1}{3} = \dfrac{2}{6} = \dfrac{3}{9} = \dfrac{\square}{12} = \dfrac{5}{\square} = \dfrac{\square}{\square}$

Now try these:

(c) $\qquad \dfrac{1}{4} = \dfrac{2}{8} = \dfrac{\square}{12} = \dfrac{\square}{16} = \dfrac{5}{\square} = \dfrac{\square}{\square}$

(d) $\qquad \dfrac{2}{5} = \dfrac{4}{10} = \dfrac{6}{15} = \dfrac{8}{20} = \dfrac{\square}{25} = \dfrac{12}{\square} = \dfrac{\square}{\square}$

Shade the amount which this sequence of fractions represents.

Multiplying by 10

When you multiply a whole number by 10 you can see that a zero is put into the units column and that the other figures move one place to the left:

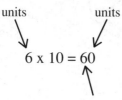

$$6 \times 10 = 60 \qquad\qquad 218 \times 10 = 2180$$

The figure 6 was in the units column but it has now moved one place to the left of the units, into the tens column.

The figure 8 was in the units column but it has now moved one place to the left of the units, into the tens column. The figure 1 has moved from the tens into the hundreds and the figure 2 has moved from the hundreds into the thousands column.

Try these multiplications by 10:

(a) $7 \times 10 =$ (b) $29 \times 10 =$ (c) $58 \times 10 =$

(d) $123 \times 10 =$ (e) $418 \times 10 =$ (f) $25 \times 10 =$

Look what happens when you multiply a decimal number by 10:

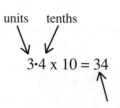

$$3{\cdot}4 \times 10 = 34 \qquad\quad 2{\cdot}75 \times 10 = 27{\cdot}5 \qquad\quad 29{\cdot}8 \times 10 = 298$$

The figure 3 was in the units column but it has now moved one place to the left of the units, into the tens column. The figure 4 was in the tenths column and it has also moved one place to the left, into the units column.

When multiplying decimals by 10 a useful trick is to move the decimal point one place to the right.

Try some more multiplications by 10:

(g) $16 \times 10 =$ (h) $4{\cdot}3 \times 10 =$ (i) $16{\cdot}7 \times 10 =$

(j) $39 \times 10 =$ (k) $3{\cdot}84 \times 10 =$ (l) $17{\cdot}75 \times 10 =$

(m) $106{\cdot}2 \times 10 =$ (n) $147 \times 10 =$ (o) $0{\cdot}9 \times 10 =$

Multiplying by 100

When you multiply a whole number by 100:

$$2 \times 100 = 200 \qquad 47 \times 100 = 4700 \qquad 867 \times 100 = 86700$$

When you multiply a whole number by 100 you can see that:

a zero is put into the units column

a zero is put into the tens column

the other figures move two places to the left

When you multiply a **decimal** number by 100 a useful trick is to **move the point two places to the right**:

$$0 \cdot 7 \times 100 = 70 \cdot 0 \qquad 6 \cdot 9 \times 100 = 690 \qquad 4 \cdot 75 \times 100 = 475$$

Try these multiplications by 100:

(a) $7 \times 100 =$

(b) $27 \times 100 =$

(c) $214 \times 100 =$

(d) $3 \cdot 5 \times 100 =$

(e) $9 \cdot 57 \times 100 =$

(f) $86 \cdot 39 \times 100 =$

(g) $0 \cdot 752 \times 100 =$

(h) $49 \times 100 =$

Multiplying by multiples of 10 or 100

Multiplying by multiples of 10 can be done in much the same way.

Multiplying by 20 can be done in two stages: **multiply by 2 then by 10**

24 x 20 is done as $24 \times 2 = 48$, then $48 \times 10 = \textbf{480}$

Look at multiplying by 300:

36 x 300 is done as $36 \times 3 = 108$, then $108 \times 100 = \textbf{10800}$

More questions to calculate:

(a) 37 x 30 = (b) 43 x 400 = (c) 19 x 5000 =

(d) 99 x 20 = (e) 123 x 3000 = (f) 52 x 600 =

(g) 6·7 x 40 = (h) 2·75 x 200 = (i) 1·5 x 3000 =

(j) Kerb-stones are 1·5 metres long.
     What is the total length of 100 kerb-stones?

(k) New maths books are £3·50 each.
     How much would a school pay for 30 copies of the book?

(l) I counted 17 different chocolates in a box.
     How many chocolates would there be altogether
     in 200 of these boxes?

Multiplying by 1000

Look at the effect of multiplying numbers by 1000:

    4 x 1000 = 4000   69 x 1000 = 69000   392 x 1000 = 392000

    6·3 x 1000 = 6300   0·406 x 1000 = 406   3·74 x 1000 = 3740

The trick here is to move the decimal point three places to the right.

Work out the answers to these questions:

(m) 32 x 100 = (n) 64 x 1000 =

(o) 543 x 10 = (p) 6·45 x 10 =

(q) 22·7 x 10 = (r) 9·678 x 1000 =

(s) 13·521 x 100 = (t) 83·2 x 100 =

(u) 7·3 x 1000 = (v) 47 x 300 =

(w) 4·75 x 60 = (x) 7 x 5000 =

(y) 23 x 400 = (z) 99 x 9000 =

Dividing by multiples of 10 or 100 or 1000

Dividing is the opposite to multiplying so the opposite happens.
When you divide any number by 10 the figures
    move one place to the right to give a smaller answer:

$$2180 \div 10 = 218$$

$$36 \cdot 7 \div 10 = 3 \cdot 67$$

Can you see what has happened here?

The nought has been removed.
The 8 has moved one place to
the right, from the tens to the
units. The 1 has moved to the
tens and the 2 has moved to the
hundreds.

Look what happens when you divide by 100 or 1000:

$$39800 \div 100 = 398 \qquad 764 \div 100 = 7 \cdot 64$$

$$465000 \div 1000 = 465 \qquad 8214 \div 1000 = 8 \cdot 214$$

The trick here is to imagine
that the decimal point has
moved **three** places to the left.

Write down the answers to these questions:

(a) $6900 \div 10 =$ (b) $31000 \div 1000 =$ (c) $28000 \div 100 =$

(d) $430 \div 100 =$ (e) $6 \cdot 14 \div 10 =$ (f) $91 \cdot 02 \div 1000 =$

(g) $3 \cdot 8 \div 1000 =$ (h) $0 \cdot 6 \div 100 =$ (i) $45 \div 10 =$

Dividing by multiples of 10, 100 or 1000 can be done in much the same way.

Dividing by 20 can be done in two stages: **divide by 10 then by 2**.

$$540 \div 20 \text{ is done as } 540 \div 10 = 54, \ 54 \div 2 = 27$$

Look at dividing by 300:

$$7200 \div 300 \text{ is done as } 7200 \div 100 = 72, \ 72 \div 3 = 24$$

More questions to calculate:

(j) $930 \div 30 =$ (k) $6400 \div 400 =$ (l) $40000 \div 5000 =$

(m) $4800 \div 600 =$ (n) $76000 \div 2000 =$ (o) $8100 \div 90 =$

Coordinates

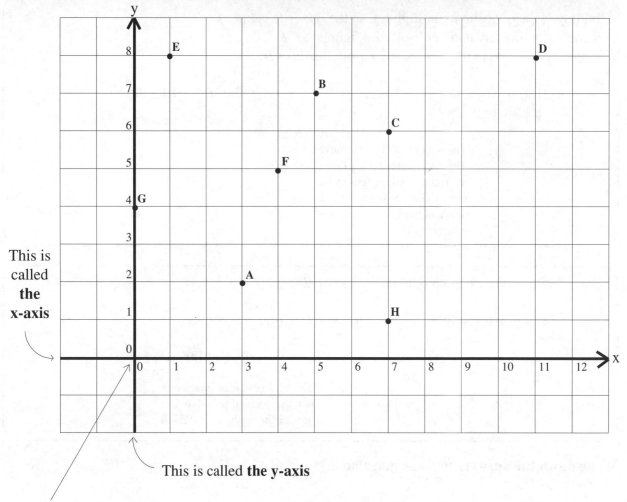

This is called **the x-axis**

This is called **the y-axis**

This point, where x is worth zero and y is worth zero, is called **the origin**. The **coordinates** of the origin are **(0, 0)**.

The coordinates of a point are given by a pair of numbers in brackets.
The **first** number tells you how far to move horizontally (in the **x** direction) from the origin.
The **second** number tells you how far to move vertically (in the **y** direction).

(a)   Point **A** is identified by the coordinates   **(3, 2)**
(b)   Point **B** is identified by the coordinates   **(5, 7)**

Identify the coordinates of points C, D, E, F, G and H.

(c)   Point **C** is identified by the coordinates   (,)
(d)   Point **D** is identified by the coordinates   (,)
(e)   Point **E** is identified by the coordinates   (,)
(f)   Point **F** is identified by the coordinates   (,)
(g)   Point **G** is identified by the coordinates   (,)
(h)   Point **H** is identified by the coordinates   (,)

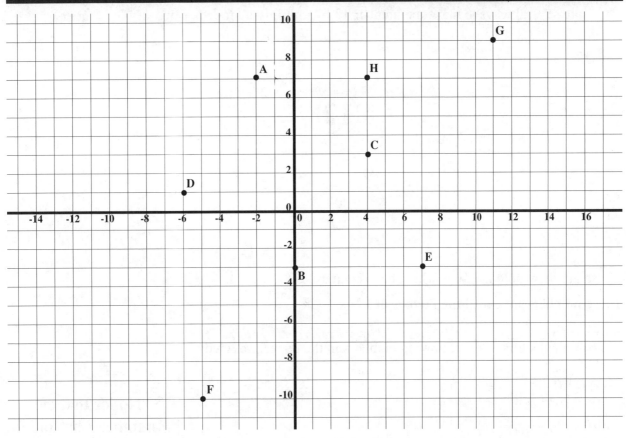

Here the x-axis has been extended to the left and the y-axis has been extended down the page.
We can now use coordinates which have negative numbers.
The **x-coordinate** of point A is -2.   The **y-coordinate** of point A is 7.

(a)   Point **A** is identified by the coordinates   **(-2, 7)**
(b)   Point **B** is identified by the coordinates   **(0, -3)**

Identify the coordinates of points C, D, E, F, G and H.

(c)   Point **C** is identified by the coordinates   (,)
(d)   Point **D** is identified by the coordinates   (,)
(e)   Point **E** is identified by the coordinates   (,)
(f)   Point **F** is identified by the coordinates   (,)
(g)   Point **G** is identified by the coordinates   (,)
(h)   Point **H** is identified by the coordinates   (,)

The points A, C, B and D make a square. Can you identify the coordinates of the point where the diagonal from A to B and the diagonal from C to D cross?

(i)   The diagonals AB and CD cross at the point   (,)

Factors and Prime Numbers

There are several ways to make the number 12 by multiplying together two whole numbers:

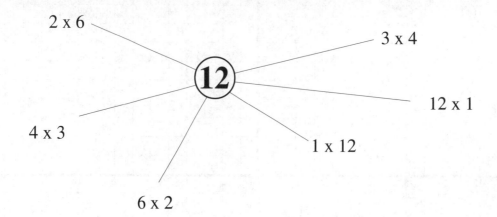

These are the whole numbers which have been used: **1, 2, 3, 4, 6, 12**

These numbers are called **the factors of 12**.

Write the factors of the following numbers in the boxes provided:

(a) 10   ☐ ☐ ☐ ☐

(b) 8   ☐ ☐ ☐ ☐

(c) 9   ☐ ☐ ☐

(d) 18   ☐ ☐ ☐ ☐ ☐ ☐

(e) 7   ☐ ☐

(f) 6   ☐ ☐ ☐ ☐

(g) 14   ☐ ☐ ☐ ☐

> Notice that the number 7 has only two factors, **itself** and **1**.
>
> Because of this it is called a **prime number**.

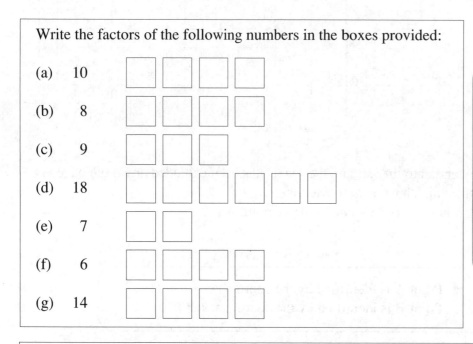

Find the factors of the following numbers:

(h) 11   ☐ ☐

(i) 4   ☐ ☐ ☐

(j) 16   ☐ ☐ ☐ ☐ ☐

(k) 5   ☐ ☐

(l) 24   ☐ ☐ ☐ ☐ ☐ ☐ ☐ ☐

(m) 19   ☐ ☐

(n) 2   ☐ ☐

Which of these numbers are prime numbers: 11   4   16   5   24   19   2 ?
Write the answers in the circles provided:

◯ ◯ ◯ ◯

Prime Numbers

Prime numbers are special because they have exactly two factors, themselves and 1.

1 is not prime because it has only one factor.

Prime numbers are unusual in that they do not make a pattern.

A Greek astronomer named **Eratostenes**, who lived 2100 years ago,
devised the following method for finding prime numbers.
It is called **the sieve of Eratostenes**.

Using the grid below:

(i)   **Cross out** the number **1** as it is not prime.
(ii) Leave 2 as it is a prime number but **cross out every multiple of 2** (4, 6, 8 ...)
(iii) Leave 3 as it is a prime number but **cross out every multiple of 3** (6, 9, 12 ...)
(iv) Leave 5 as it is a prime number but **cross out every multiple of 5** (10, 15 ...)
(iii) Leave 7 as it is a prime number but **cross out every multiple of 7** (14, 21 ...)

1	2	3	4	5	6	7	8	9	10
11	12	13	14	15	16	17	18	19	20
21	22	23	24	25	26	27	28	29	30
31	32	33	34	35	36	37	38	39	40
41	42	43	44	45	46	47	48	49	50
51	52	53	54	55	56	57	58	59	60
61	62	63	64	65	66	67	68	69	70
71	72	73	74	75	76	77	78	79	80
81	82	83	84	85	86	87	88	89	90
91	92	93	94	95	96	97	98	99	100

The numbers which are left uncrossed are all prime numbers.

(a) List all the prime numbers between 1 and 100:

(b) What is the only **even** prime number?

Multiplication

Complete the following multiplications:

(a) 34	(b) 27	(c) 89	(d) 168	(e) 214
x 3	x 4	x 6	x 7	x 9

(f) 972	(g) 539	(h) 804	(i) 75	(j) 99
x 8	x 5	x 2	x 6	x 9

In the above multiplications you were multiplying by **units** only.

For example, in question (e) you had to first multiply 4 units **by 9 units**, then 1 ten **by 9 units**, then 2 hundreds **by 9 units**.

Now look at this question:

```
   34
x 20
```

Here we need to multiply **by 2 tens**.

```
   34
x 20
_____
    0
```

The first thing we do is put a zero in the units column.

Now we multiply 4 by 2 to give 8 in the tens column.

```
   34
x 20
_____
   80
```

.... then 3 by 2 to give 6 in the hundreds.

```
   34
x 20
_____
 680
```

Complete the following multiplications:

(k) 42	(l) 27	(m) 89	(n) 267	(o) 893
x 20	x 40	x 30	x 50	x 60

(p) 343	(q) 78	(r) 908	(s) 418	(t) 999
x 90	x 40	x 20	x 60	x 80

Long Multiplication

Sometimes we need to multiply by tens and units together.

We use a method called **long multiplication**:

$$\begin{array}{r} 47 \\ \times\ 23 \\ \hline \end{array}$$

To do this question we must multiply by the 3 units first:

$$\begin{array}{r} 47 \\ \times\ 23 \\ \hline 141 \end{array}$$

Then we multiply by the 2 tens, putting the answer underneath.

$$\begin{array}{r} 47 \\ \times\ 23 \\ \hline 141 \\ 940 \end{array}$$

Now we add the two answers which we have found to give the final answer to the question.

$$\begin{array}{r} 47 \\ \times\ 23 \\ \hline 141 \\ 940 \\ \hline 1081 \end{array}$$

Complete the following multiplications:

(a)
$$\begin{array}{r} 62 \\ \times\ 31 \\ \hline \end{array}$$

(b)
$$\begin{array}{r} 43 \\ \times\ 24 \\ \hline \end{array}$$

(c)
$$\begin{array}{r} 94 \\ \times\ 62 \\ \hline \end{array}$$

(d)
$$\begin{array}{r} 197 \\ \times\ 34 \\ \hline \end{array}$$

(e)
$$\begin{array}{r} 428 \\ \times\ 37 \\ \hline \end{array}$$

(f)
$$\begin{array}{r} 297 \\ \times\ 85 \\ \hline \end{array}$$

(g)
$$\begin{array}{r} 539 \\ \times\ 59 \\ \hline \end{array}$$

(h)
$$\begin{array}{r} 721 \\ \times\ 99 \\ \hline \end{array}$$

(i)
$$\begin{array}{r} 684 \\ \times\ 48 \\ \hline \end{array}$$

(j)
$$\begin{array}{r} 912 \\ \times\ 74 \\ \hline \end{array}$$

(k)
$$\begin{array}{r} 27 \\ \times\ 27 \\ \hline \end{array}$$

(l)
$$\begin{array}{r} 56 \\ \times\ 56 \\ \hline \end{array}$$

(m)
$$\begin{array}{r} 12 \\ \times\ 12 \\ \hline \end{array}$$

Index Numbers or Powers

An **index number** is a small number at the top right hand side of another: 3^2

The number 2 is called an index number.

The index number shows how many times the other number is multiplied by itself.......

.... 3^2 means 3 x 3 so $3^2 = 9$

.... 10^3 means 10 x 10 x 10 so $10^3 = 1000$

.... 10^4 means 10 x 10 x 10 x 10 so $10^4 = 10,000$

Evaluate (work out) the following without using a calculator:

(a) $3^4 =$ (b) $2^5 =$ (c) $11^2 =$ (d) $4^3 =$

(e) $10^6 =$ (f) $1^2 =$ (g) $2^7 =$ (h) $5^3 =$

Another word for an index number is a **power**. We say that 10^3 and 10^4 are **powers of ten**.

We can read 6^4 as "six **to the power four**" or 8^5 as "eight **to the power five**".

Powers of two and three have their own names:

4^2 can be read as four to the power two or "**four squared**"

5^3 can be read as five to the power three or "**five cubed**"

Square Numbers

Evaluate the following square numbers without using a calculator:

(i) $6^2 =$ (j) $9^2 =$ (k) $3^2 =$ (l) $8^2 =$

(m) $7^2 =$ (n) $4^2 =$ (o) $2^2 =$ (p) $5^2 =$

Look back at page 15 to find the answers to these questions:

(q) $56^2 =$ (r) $12^2 =$ (s) $27^2 =$

Use long multiplication to work out the values of the following square numbers:

(a) 13^2

$$\begin{array}{r} 13 \\ \times\ 13 \\ \hline \end{array}$$

_____

_____

(b) 14^2

$$\begin{array}{r} 14 \\ \times\ 14 \\ \hline \end{array}$$

_____

_____

(c) 15^2

$$\begin{array}{r} 15 \\ \times\ 15 \\ \hline \end{array}$$

_____

_____

(d) 16^2

$$\begin{array}{r} 16 \\ \times\ 16 \\ \hline \end{array}$$

_____

_____

(e) 20^2

$$\begin{array}{r} 20 \\ \times\ 20 \\ \hline \end{array}$$

_____

_____

(f) 25^2

$$\begin{array}{r} 25 \\ \times\ 25 \\ \hline \end{array}$$

_____

_____

Cube Numbers

To find the values of cube numbers, follow this example:

$$6^3$$

Firstly we must multiply 6 by 6 to give **36**

Then we multiply the 36 by 6:

$$\begin{array}{r} 36 \\ \times\ \ 6 \\ \hline 216 \end{array}$$

.... so 6^3 = **216**

Evaluate the following cube numbers without using a calculator:

(g) $2^3 =$

(h) $7^3 =$

(i) $4^3 =$

(j) $9^3 =$

(k) $5^3 =$

(l) $3^3 =$

(m) $8^3 =$

(n) $10^3 =$

Lines and Angles

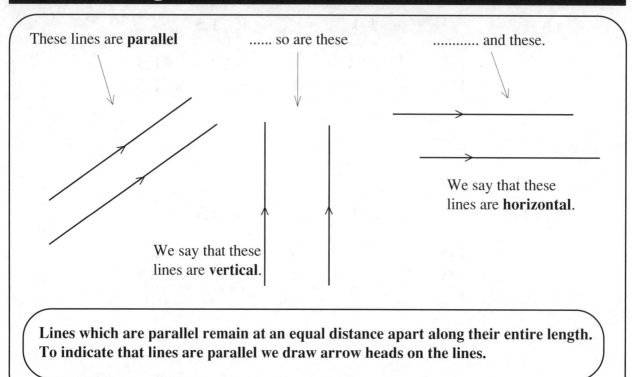

These lines are **parallel** ...... so are these .... and these.

We say that these lines are **horizontal**.

We say that these lines are **vertical**.

Lines which are parallel remain at an equal distance apart along their entire length. To indicate that lines are parallel we draw arrow heads on the lines.

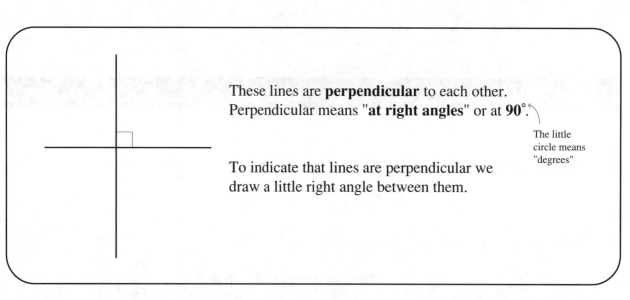

These lines are **perpendicular** to each other. Perpendicular means "**at right angles**" or at **90°**.

The little circle means "degrees"

To indicate that lines are perpendicular we draw a little right angle between them.

Look at these pairs of lines:

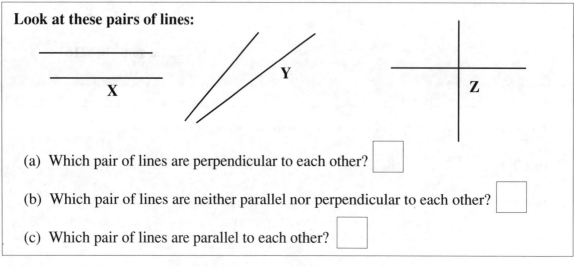

X

Y

Z

(a) Which pair of lines are perpendicular to each other?

(b) Which pair of lines are neither parallel nor perpendicular to each other?

(c) Which pair of lines are parallel to each other?

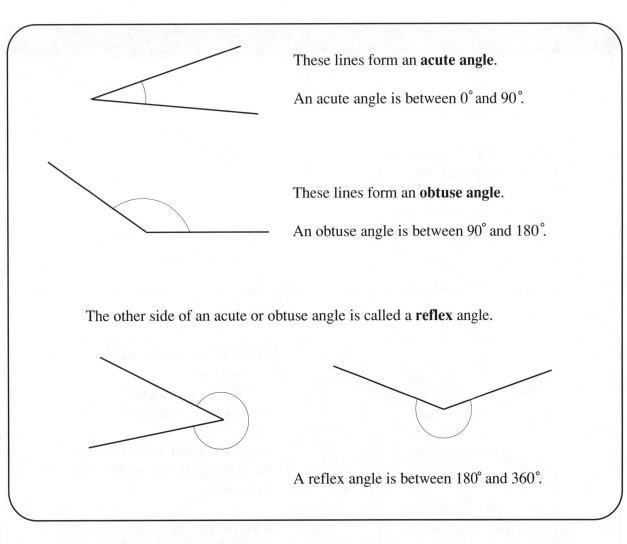

These lines form an **acute angle**.

An acute angle is between 0° and 90°.

These lines form an **obtuse angle**.

An obtuse angle is between 90° and 180°.

The other side of an acute or obtuse angle is called a **reflex** angle.

A reflex angle is between 180° and 360°.

Look at each of these angles. Write 'acute', 'obtuse' or 'reflex' for each angle.

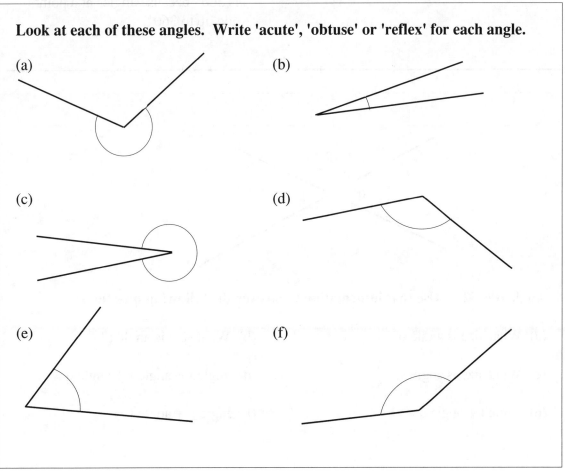

(a)

(b)

(c)

(d)

(e)

(f)

More Lines and Angles

When two lines **intersect** (cross) they make four angles.

An opposite pair of angles are called **vertically opposite**. As you can see from the diagram, they do not have to be in a vertical line.

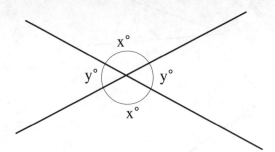

Vertically opposite angles are equal in size.

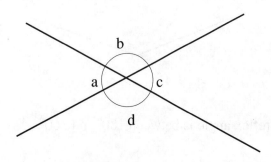

Vertically opposite angles are equal in size ......
.... so **angle a = angle c** and **angle b = angle d**.

If you add **a** and **b** the total is $180°$ because angles on a straight line add up to $180°$.

If you add all four angles the total is $360°$ because angles at a point add up to $360°$.

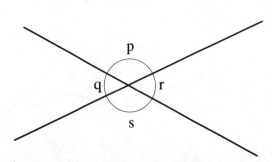

Angle q is 52°.   Use that information to answer the following questions:

(a) What size is angle p? ☐

(b) What size is angle r? ☐

(c) What size is angle s? ☐

(d) angle r + angle s + angle q = ☐

(e) angle r + angle q = ☐

(f) angle p + angle s = ☐

The size of this acute angle is shown.
Use a protractor to check the size.

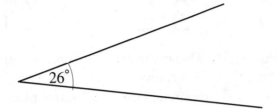

Measure these acute angles and write down the size of each.

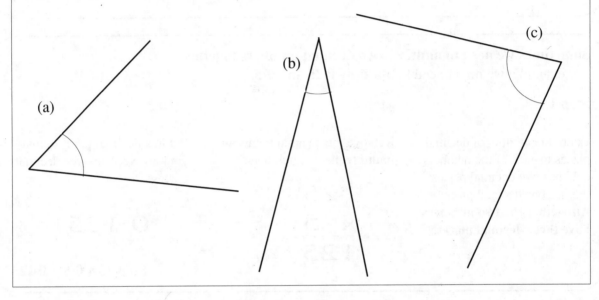

Measure these obtuse angles and write down the size of each.

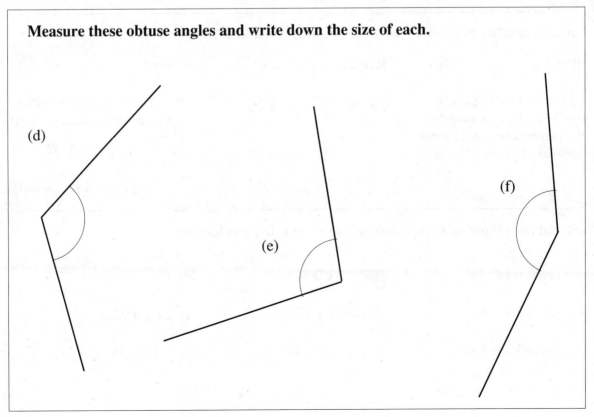

Decimal Places and Multiplication

6·45
We say that this number has **two decimal places** because there are two digits **after** the decimal point.

3·2
This number has **one** decimal place.

0·75
This number has **two** decimal places.

0·8
This number has **one** decimal place.

23·3
This number has **one** decimal place.

23·7941
This number has **four** decimal places.

Sometimes we need to multiply two decimal numbers together.
For example, we might need to **multiply 0·25 and 0·5**:

Step 1

Count the number of decimal places in each of the numbers: 0·25 has two decimal places; 0·5 has one decimal place. **Altogether the two numbers have three decimal places.**

Step 2

Remove the decimal points and multiply the two numbers:

$$\begin{array}{r} 25 \\ \times\ 5 \\ \hline 125 \end{array}$$

Step 3

Put in a decimal point so that your answer has three decimal places:

$$0·125$$

So 0·25 x 0·5 = 0·125

Look at another example: we need to **multiply 6 and 0·003**:

Step 1

6 has no decimal places but 0·003 has three so **altogether the two numbers have three decimal places.**

Step 2

$$6 \times 3 = 18$$

Step 3

Put in a decimal point so that your answer has three decimal places:

$$0·018$$

So 6 x 0·003 = 0·018

Work out the following multiplications without using a calculator:

(a) 0·6 x 0·7 =

(b) 12 x 0·34 =

(c) 8 x 6·2 =

(d) 4·3 x 2·9 =

(e) 6·35 x 2·4 =

(f) 24 x 0·97 =

(g) 8·5 x 4·5 =

(h) 1·75 x 4 =

(i) 7·8 x 0·35 =

(j) 1·6 x 3·2 x 0·5 =

(k) 7 x 3·1 x 0·07 =

Division and Decimals

Very often when we divide two numbers we find that there is a remainder:

$$\begin{array}{r} 73 \text{ r } 1 \\ 2\overline{)147} \end{array}$$

Complete the following divisions, leaving a remainder if appropriate:

(a)

$$5\overline{)342}$$

(b)

$$7\overline{)286}$$

(c)

$$6\overline{)798}$$

(d)

$$8\overline{)500}$$

(e)

$$3\overline{)416}$$

(f)

$$4\overline{)2842}$$

(g) There are 214 pupils and 7 teachers having school lunch. Each table can seat 8 people. How many tables are needed?

Sometimes we need an exact answer and we do not want any remainder:

$$\begin{array}{r} 73 \text{ r } 1 \\ 2\overline{)147} \end{array}$$

Instead of having the 1 unit left over we can break it up into 10 tenths giving an answer with 1 decimal place:

$$\begin{array}{r} 73 \cdot 5 \\ 2\overline{)147 \cdot {}^1 0} \end{array}$$

Complete the following divisions, giving answers with decimal places:

(h)

$$2\overline{)15}$$

(i)

$$4\overline{)57}$$

(j)

$$8\overline{)95}$$

(k)

$$3\overline{)87 \cdot 6}$$

(l)

$$5\overline{)319}$$

(m)

$$7\overline{)16 \cdot 38}$$

Decimal Places and Division

If we divide 8 by 5 we will find an answer with one decimal place:

$$\begin{array}{r} 1 \cdot 6 \\ 5 \overline{)8 \cdot {}^{3}0} \end{array}$$

If we divide 5 by 8 we will find an answer with three decimal places:

$$\begin{array}{r} 0 \cdot 625 \\ 8 \overline{)5 \cdot 0{}^{2}0{}^{4}0} \end{array}$$

Complete the following divisions:

(a)

$$6 \overline{)3}$$

(b)

$$8 \overline{)3}$$

(c)

$$4 \overline{)3}$$

(d)

$$4 \overline{)27}$$

(e)

$$8 \overline{)25}$$

(f)

$$2 \overline{)163 \cdot 7}$$

If we divide 1 by 3 we will find an answer which repeats forever:

$$\begin{array}{r} 0 \cdot 3333333 \ldots\ldots\ldots \\ 3 \overline{)1 \cdot {}^{1}0{}^{1}0{}^{1}0{}^{1}0{}^{1}0{}^{1}0{}^{1}0} \ldots\ldots\ldots \end{array}$$

Obviously we cannot go on forever so we write the answer like this: $0 \cdot \dot{3}$

The dot over the 3 shows that it is a **recurring** number.

Try these divisions. Watch for where they repeat.

(g)

$$3 \overline{)8}$$

(h)

$$6 \overline{)19}$$

(i)

$$9 \overline{)80}$$

(j)

$$7 \overline{)22}$$

Page 2 a 29, 35   b 19, 10   c 18, 27   d 8, 4   e 27,81   f $\frac{5}{6}$, $\frac{6}{7}$

g 25, 36   h 33, 65   i 12, 30   j 8, 9

Page 3 a 2036   b 3530   c 5021   d 8859   e 3006

f 7658   g 57·35   h 1220·68   i 52·43   j 366·46

Page 4 a 553   b 2327   c 1409   d 6076   e 175259

f 5581   g 13·5   h 3·45   i 5·05   j 5·3   k 115·41   l 998·3

Page 5 a $\frac{4}{8}$ $\frac{5}{10}$ $\frac{6}{12}$ b $\frac{4}{12}$ $\frac{5}{15}$ $\frac{6}{18}$ c $\frac{3}{12}$ $\frac{4}{16}$ $\frac{5}{20}$ $\frac{6}{24}$ d $\frac{10}{25}$ $\frac{12}{30}$ $\frac{14}{35}$ 2 sections shaded

Page 6 a 70   b 290   c 580   d 1230   e 4180   f 250

g 160   h 43   i 167   j 390   k 38·4   l 177·5

m 1062   n 1470   o 9

Page 7 a 700   b 2700   c 21400   d 350   e 957   f 8639   g 75·2   h 4900

Page 8 a 1110   b 17200   c 95000   d 1980   e 369000   f 31200   g 268   h 550

i 4500   j 150 m   k £105   l 3400   m 3200   n 64000   o 5430   p 64·5

q 227   r 9678   s 1352·1   t 8320   u 7300   v 14100   w 285   x 35000

y 9200   z 891000

Page 9 a 690   b 31   c 280   d 4·3   e 0·614   f 0·09102   g 0·0038   h 0·006

i 4·5   j 31   k 16   l 8   m 8   n 38   o 90

Page 10 C = (7, 6)   D = (11, 8)   E = (1, 8)   F = (4, 5)   G = (0, 4)   H = (7, 1)

Page 11 C = (4, 3)   D = (- 6, 1)   E = (7, - 3)   F = (- 5, - 10)   G = (11, 9)   H = (4, 7)   i (- 1, 2)

Page 12 a 1 2 5 10   b 1 2 4 8   c 1 3 9   d 1 2 3 6 9 18   e 1 7   f 1 2 3 6

g 1 2 7 14   h 1 11   i 1 2 4   j 1 2 4 8 16   k 1 5   l 1 2 3 4 6 8 12 24

m 1 19   n 1 2   primes: 11 5 19 2

Page 13 a 2 3 5 7 11 13 17 19 23 29 31 37 41 43 47 53 59 61 67 71 73 79 83 89 97

b 2

Page 14 a 102   b 108   c 534   d 1176   e 1926   f 7776   g 2695   h 1608

i 450   j 891   k 840   l 1080   m 2670   n 13350   o 53580   p 30870

q 3120   r 18160   s 25080   t 79920

Page 15 a 1922   b 1032   c 5828   d 6698   e 15836   f 25245   g 31801   h 71379

i 32832   j 67488   k 729   l 3136   m 144

Page 16   a 81   b 32   c 121   d 64   e 1000000   ƒ 1   g 128   h 125

i 36   j 81   k 9   l 64   m 49   n 16   o 4   p 25

q 3136   r 144   s 729

Page 17   a 169   b 196   c 225   d 256   e 400   ƒ 625   g 8   h 343

i 64   j 729   k 125   l 27   m 512   n 1000

Page 18   a Z   b Y   c X

Page 19   a reflex   b acute   c reflex   d obtuse   e acute   ƒ obtuse

Page 20   a 128°   b 52°   c 128°   d 232°   e 104°   ƒ 256°

Page 21   a 51°   b 27°   c 77°   d 121°   e 99°   ƒ 149°

Page 22   a 0·42   b 4·08   c 49·6   d 12·47   e 15·24 (or 15·240)   ƒ 23·28   g 38·25

h 7 or (7·00)   i 2·73 (or 2·730)   j 2·56 (or 2·560)   k 1·519

Page 23   a 68 rem 2   b 40 rem 6   c 133   d 62 rem 4   e 138 rem 2   ƒ 710 rem 2

g 28 tables   h 7·5   i 14·25   j 11·875   k 29·2   l 63·8   m 2·34

Page 24   a 0·5   b 0·375   c 0·75   d 6·75   e 3·125   ƒ 81·85

g $2\cdot\dot{6}$ h $3\cdot\dot{1}\dot{6}$ i $8\cdot\dot{8}$ j $3\cdot\dot{1}4285\dot{7}$ (note: where a string of numerals repeats we place a dot over the first and last numbers of the string)

Page 25   a 14·4   b 5·2   c 6·4   d 118·9   e 23·5   ƒ 9·1   g 400·6   h 0·3

Page 26   a 82·4   b 7·1   c 28·0   d 101·9   e 64·33   ƒ 4·33   g 17·92   h 54·80

i 10·667   j 7·143   k 2·439   l 14·074

Page 27   a 4   b 7   c 10   d 9   e 5   ƒ 2   g 6   h 14

i 3   j 13   k 8   l 20

Page 28   a 1024   b 12·96   c 299·29   d 6241   e 18·0625   ƒ 75·69   g 11   h 10·54

i 7·5   j 3·81   k 7·92   l 8·37

Page 29   a 12 m^2 b $11\cdot34 \text{ m}^2$ c $9\cdot19 \text{ cm}^2$ d $10\cdot08 \text{ m}^2$ e $13\cdot69 \text{ cm}^2$

Page 30   a $15 \text{ cm}^2 + 20 \text{ cm}^2 + 8 \text{ cm}^2 = 43 \text{ cm}^2$ b $80\cdot9 \text{ cm}^2$

Page 31   a 72 cm^3 b 2375 cm^3 c 729 cm^3

Page 32   a 21 °C   b - 2 °C   c - 15 °C

Page 33   a 10 °C   b - 4 °C   c - 1 °C   d 9 m   e 0·5 m   ƒ 9·5 m   g - 12 m

Page 35   a 6200 mm   b 7800 ml   c 1·1 g   d 6720 m   e 125 ml   f 1·16 m

g 2·25 kg   h 39·62 m   i 135 mm   j 6·32 cm   k 0·875 l   l 1·55 m   m 3 m

n 50 g   o 1·98 l   p 11·7 cm   q 25   r 3·2 km   s 3·438 t

Page 36   a 880 yds   b 48 in.   c 66 ft.

Page 37   a 4'6"   b 4'6"   c 28 yds 1ft 10 in   d 5 galls 3pts   e 16   f 3 galls   g 14 galls 2 pts

Page 38   a 104 lb   b 3 lb 12 oz   c 112 lb   d 98 lb   e 12 oz

Page 39   a 3 m by 2 m   b 30 cm   c 24 km   d 10 m   e 14 in by 8 in

Page 40   a $3\frac{1}{2}$ pts   b $10\frac{1}{2}$ galls   c 11   d 40 lb   e 125 g   f £5·40

Page 41   a 4   b 6   c 1   d 5   e 3   f C M X Y

Page 42   a 4   b 6   c 1   d 5   e 3

        If a shape has lines of symmetry it also has rotational symmetry
              but the opposite is not necessarily true.

Page 43   a 64   b 58   c 38   d 48   e 111   f 172   g 246   h 145

Page 44   a 18   b 5   c 90   d 160   e 368   f 200   g 300   h 1·4

i 12   j 81

Page 45   a 37   b 7   c 27 cm   d 23 mm

Page 46   a 41   b 11   c 42 cm   d 17 cm

Page 47   a 3   b 14   c 14   d 19   e 15 & 25   f $19\frac{1}{2}$

Page 48   a The first set has no mode. The second set has: 181.

b (i) 146, 150, 152, 155, 157, 158, 160   median 155 cm
   (ii) 149, 152, 173, 174, 180, 181,181   median 174 cm

c The median of the second set is 19 cm larger than the first median.
  The second set of people are generally taller than the first set.

d (i) 14 cm   (ii) 32 cm

e The heights of the second set are more widely spread than the first set.

More Decimal Places

Sometimes a number will have more decimal places than are needed.
We may want to round the number up or down to 1 decimal place or to 2 decimal places.

Look at this number:

0·7

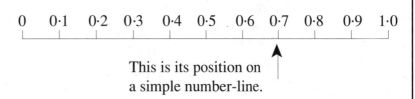

This is its position on
a simple number-line.

Now consider this number
and its position on the line:

0·79

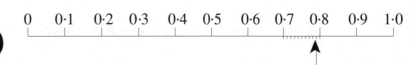

The number 0·79 has two decimal places.

If we wish to approximate it to one decimal place we would say **0·8**
because, as you can see on the number line, 0·79 is closer to 0·8 than to 0·7

We would write: **0·79 = 0·8 to 1 dp**   ('dp' stands for decimal place)

In the same way: 0·72 = 0·7 to 1dp   (because on the line 0·72 is closer to 0·7)
0·76 = 0·8 to 1dp   (because on the line 0·76 is closer to 0·8)

Look at this number
and its position on the line:

0·75

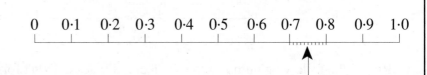

The number 0·75 is exactly half-way between 0·7 and 0·8.
The rule we follow is to round the number **up**. So **0·75** is approximated to **0·8 to 1dp**.

0·75 = 0·8 to 1dp

Round the following numbers to one decimal place. Don't forget to write "**to 1 dp**".

(a)   14·39 =

(b)   5·21 =

(c)   6·42 =

(d)   118·89 =

(e)   23·45 =

(f)   9·07 =

(g)   400·63 =

(h)   0·34 =

Some numbers have several decimal places but they can still be rounded up or down to 1 dp.

Look at this number: 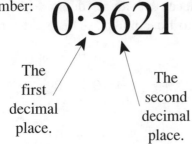 **0·3621**

The first decimal place.

The second decimal place.

We want to round the number to one decimal place so we look at the number next to the first decimal place. This is a 6 so we can round the 3 **up** to 4. We simply ignore the 2 and the 1.

$$0·3621 = 0·4 \text{ to 1dp}$$

Look how these numbers are rounded to one decimal place:

0·2189 = 0·2 to 1dp   17·067 = 17·1 to 1dp

8·44 = 8·4 to 1dp   23·49 = 23·5 to 1dp

Round the following numbers to one decimal place. Don't forget to write "**to 1 dp**".

(a)   82·364 = [　　　　]   (b)   7·064 = [　　　　]

(c)   28·049 = [　　　　]   (d)   101·94 = [　　　　]

Round the following numbers to two decimal places. Don't forget to write "**to 2 dp**".

(e)   64·326 = [　　　　]   (f)   4·3333 = [　　　　]

(g)   17·919 = [　　　　]   (h)   54·7971 = [　　　　]

Calculate these divisions and give the answers to 3 dp.
Remember to work out your answers to 4 dp so that you can round to 3 dp.

(i)

$$6\overline{)64}$$

(j)

$$7\overline{)50}$$

(k)

$$4\overline{)9·7556}$$

(l)

$$3\overline{)42·2229}$$

Squares and Square Roots

We have already looked at square numbers.

On page 2 we saw square numbers made with dot patterns:

This pattern is 5 dots wide and 5 dots long.

There are 25 dots altogether.

The pattern shows that $5^2 = 25$

On page 17 we used long multiplication to find some square numbers. For example, we calculated 16^2 and found the answer to be **256**.

Finding the **square root** of a number is the opposite of finding the square.......

.... so, for example, **the square root of 9 is 3** because $3^2 = 9$.

Find the square root of each of the following numbers:

(a) 16 ☐   (b) 49 ☐   (c) 100 ☐

(d) 81 ☐   (e) 25 ☐   (f)   4 ☐

The symbol for square root looks like a tick:

If we were finding the square root of 16, we would write: $\sqrt{16} = 4$

Answer the following questions.
Looking back to the questions which you did on page 17 should help you with some of your answers.

(g) $\sqrt{36}$ =   (h) $\sqrt{196}$ =   (i) $\sqrt{9}$ =

(j) $\sqrt{169}$ =   (k) $\sqrt{64}$ =   (l) $\sqrt{400}$ =

Note: The square root of 1 is 1 because 1 x 1 = 1.

$$1^2 = 1 \qquad \sqrt{1} = 1$$

Using your calculator

For this page you will need a **scientific** calculator.

You can use your calculator to square numbers.

To find 4^2 press the following keys:

Sometimes we need to square decimal numbers; the calculator makes this easy:

To find $2·6^2$ press the following keys:

Use your calculator to solve the following questions:

(a) $32^2 =$ (b) $3·6^2 =$ (c) $17·3^2 =$

(d) $79^2 =$ (e) $4·25^2 =$ (f) $8·7^2 =$

You can use your calculator to find the square root of numbers.

To find $\sqrt{4}$ press the following keys: **to give the answer 2**

To find $\sqrt{20}$ press the following keys:

to give the answer 4·47213 ....

If we write the answer to two decimal places we can say:

$$\sqrt{20} = 4·47 \text{ to 2 dp}$$

NOTE: ON SOME CALCULATORS YOU NEED TO PRESS THE NUMBER KEYS **BEFORE** THE SQUARE ROOT KEY.

Use your calculator to answer the following questions.
Give your answers to 2 dp where necessary.

(g) $\sqrt{121} =$ (h) $\sqrt{111} =$ (i) $\sqrt{56·25} =$

(j) $\sqrt{14·5} =$ (k) $\sqrt{62·8} =$ (l) $\sqrt{70} =$

Area

It is very easy to find the area of a square or rectangle:

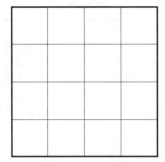

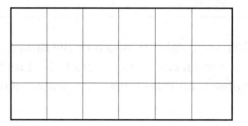

This square is 4 cm long and 4 cm wide so its area is: 4 x 4 = 16 square centimetres.
4 cm x 4 cm = 16 cm²

This rectangle is 6 cm long and 3 cm wide so its area is: 6 x 3 = 18 square centimetres.
6 cm x 3 cm = 18 cm²

(a) Here is a plan of a bedroom. Calculate its area in square metres.

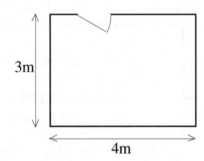

3m

4m

Area =   m²

Use your calculator to find the areas of the following shapes and plans.
If necessary give your answers to two decimal places.
Remember to write m² or cm² as appropriate.

(b)

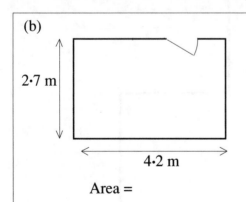

2·7 m

4·2 m

Area =

(c)

1·75 cm

5·25 cm

Area =

(d)

1·5 m

6·72 m

Area =

(e)

3·7 cm

3·7 cm

Area =

Some plans consist of quite complicated shapes.
Here it is best to split the plan into pieces.
Find the area of each piece then add these up to find the total area.

**Use your ruler to measure the dimensions of this shape,
then separate it into pieces to find its total area.
Some faint lines have been drawn to help you.**

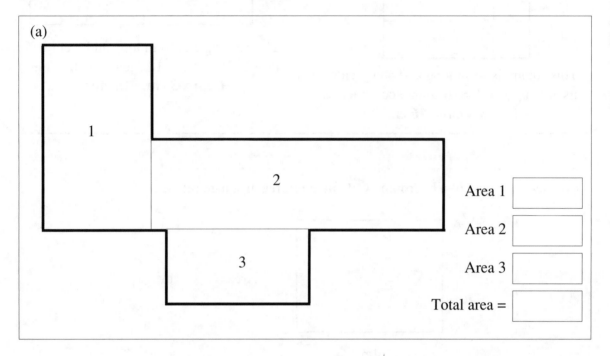

(a)

Area 1

Area 2

Area 3

Total area =

In a similar way find the total area of the next shape.

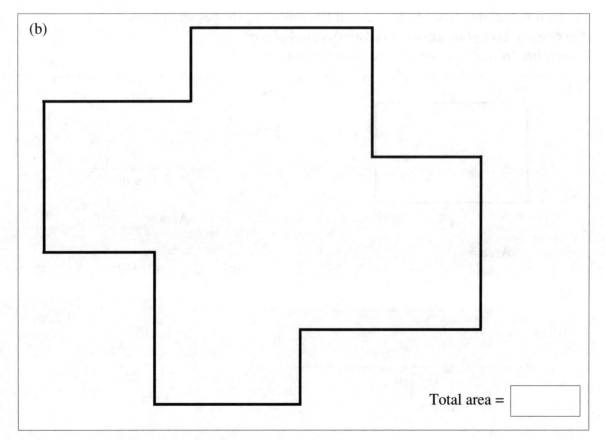

(b)

Total area =

Cubes and cuboids

This picture represents a cube where each edge is 4 metres long.

The **volume** of the cube is found by multiplying its **height**, its **width** and its **length**.

The cube is 4 m high, 4 m wide and 4 m long so its volume is:

4 x 4 x 4 = 64 cubic metres.

We can write: **Volume = 64 m^3.**

Notice the small 3 to represent 'cubic'.

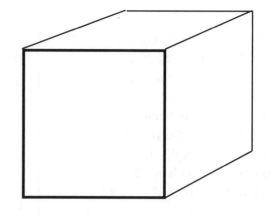

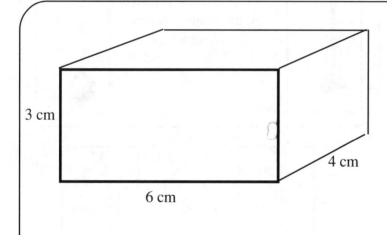

3 cm

6 cm

4 cm

This picture represents a cuboid. Each side of a cuboid is a rectangle.

The volume of the cuboid is also found by multiplying its **height**, its **width** and its **length**.

We can shorten this to:

V = H x W x L

We would write the answer in cubic centimetres: **cm^3**

Answer these questions about volume.

Remember to give your answer in cubic metres or cubic centimetres.

(a) What is the volume of the cuboid shown above?

(b) A cereal box is 25 cm high, 19 cm long and 5 cm wide.
      What is the volume of the cereal box?

(c) A block of notepaper is in the shape of a cube.
      Each edge of the block measures 9 cm.
        What is the volume of the block?

Using negative numbers

Probably the most common everyday use of negative numbers is with temperature.

If you watch the weather forecast during the winter you will frequently see temperatures such as -2℃, -3℃ or even as cold as -8℃.

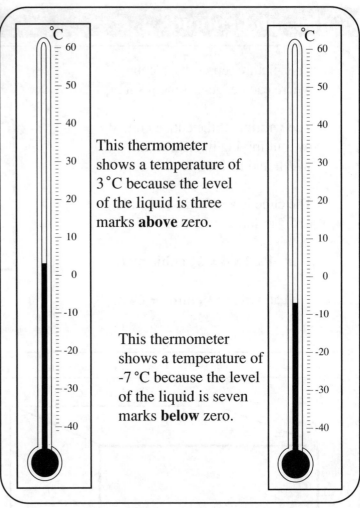

This thermometer shows a temperature of 3 ℃ because the level of the liquid is three marks **above** zero.

This thermometer shows a temperature of -7 ℃ because the level of the liquid is seven marks **below** zero.

State the temperature shown on each of the thermometers.

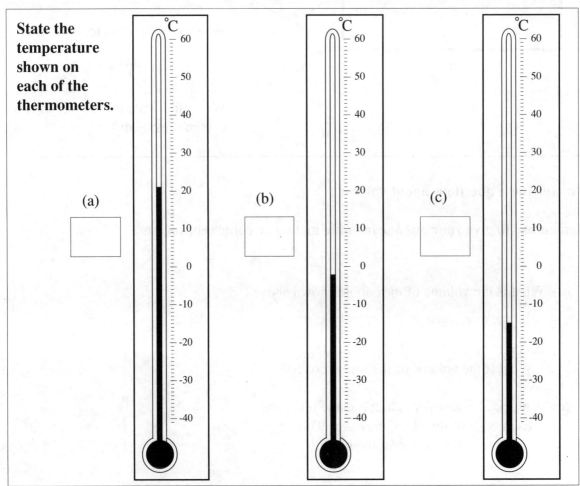

(a)

(b)

(c)

Use the picture of the thermometer on the right to help you to answer the following questions:

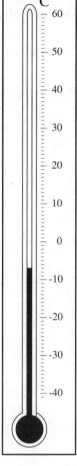

(a) If the temperature at midnight was -3°C and the temperature at midday was 7°C, by how much has the temperature risen?

(b) On a winter evening the temperature fell from 6°C by 10°C. What was the new temperature?

(c) A plane left New York where the temperature was -6°C and arrived in London where it was five degrees warmer.
What was the temperature in London?

Negative numbers can also be used to describe distances below sea-level.

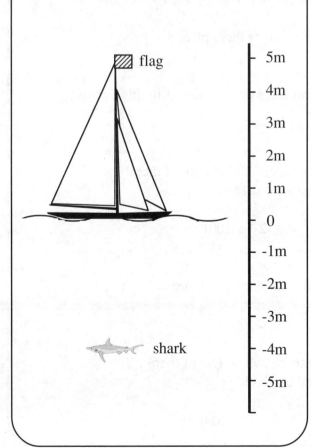

(d) What is the difference in height between the flag and the shark?

(e) What height is half way between the flag and the shark?

(f) A small fish is out of sight at -13·5m. How far below the shark is it?

(g) If the shark dives another 8 metres, at what depth will it be?

33

Metric Measurements

The basic metric units are: **metre**, **litre** and **gram**.

To each of these words we can add one of the following prefixes:

kilo, **centi** or **milli**.

meaning 1000   meaning $\frac{1}{100}$ meaning $\frac{1}{1000}$

1 **kilo**gram = 1000 grams   1 gram = 1000 **milli**grams

1 **kilo**metre = 1000 metres

1 metre = 100 **centi**metres **or** 1000 **milli**metres

1 litre = 100 **centi**litres **or** 1000 **milli**litres

Remember also that: **10 millimetres = 1 centimetre**

and: **1000 kilograms = 1 tonne**

To change between different units you either multiply or divide by 10, 100 or 1000.

This can be done by moving the decimal point one, two or three places.

For example, to change 32·1 metres to centimetres there are two things to think about:

(1)   **centi** involves 100

(2)   centimetres are smaller than metres so there will be more of them
            - this shows that you need to **multiply**

32·1 m = 3210 cm   (32·1 x 100)

To change 46·7 centimetres to metres the two things to think about are:

(1)   centi involves 100

(2)   metres are larger than centimetres so there will be less of them
            - this shows that you need to **divide**

46·7 cm = 0·467 m   (46·7 ÷ 100)

Answer all these questions about metric measurements:

(a) 6·2 m = ☐ mm   (b) 7·8 l = ☐ ml

(c) 1100 mg = ☐ g   (d) 6·72 km = ☐ m

(e) 0·125 l = ☐ ml   (f) 116 cm = ☐ m

(g) 2250 g = ☐ kg   (h) 3962 cm = ☐ m

(i) 13·5 cm = ☐ mm   (j) 63·2 mm = ☐ cm

(k) 0·125 l are poured from a 1 l bottle. How much is left? ☐

(l) 45 cm is cut from a 2 m length of wood. How much is left? ☐

(m) A piece of string is cut into twenty 15 cm lengths.
How long was the original piece of string in metres? ☐

(n) A large bar of chocolate weighing 0·6 kg is to be divided between twelve people. Change the weight to grams and then find what weight of chocolate each person receives. ☐

(o) A bottle of drink holds 330 ml. Six bottles are sold together in a pack. What is the total volume of drink, in litres? ☐

(p) A textbook is 13 mm thick. If nine books are stacked, what is the total thickness of the pile, in centimetres? ☐

(q) A bottle of medicine holds 0·125 l. How many 5 ml spoonfuls can be poured from the bottle? ☐

(r) An athlete runs around a 400 m track eight times.
How many kilometres has she run? ☐

(s) A load of 238 kg is loaded onto the back of a 3·2 tonne lorry.
What is the total weight of the lorry and its load? ☐

Imperial Measurements

The old-fashioned units of measurement are called **imperial measurements**.

Imperial measurements are more complicated than metric measurements:

For measuring **length** the imperial units are **inches**, **feet**, **yards** and **miles**.

For measuring **capacity** the imperial units are **pints**, **quarts** and **gallons**.

For measuring **weight** the imperial units are **ounces**, **pounds**, **stones**, **hundredweights** and **tons**.

Length

12 inches = 1 foot   This can be written in other ways: **12" = 1'**   or   **12 in = 1 ft**

3 feet = 1 yard   ....   **3' = 1 yd**   or   **3 ft = 1 yd**

1760 yards = 1 mile   ....   **1760 yds = 1 m**

Answer the following questions:

(a)   How many yards are there in half a mile?

(b)   How many inches are there in four feet?

(c)   A cricket pitch is 22 yards long. Change this to feet.

Don't forget that **12 inches make a foot** when you look at the following example:

One plank is 4 ft 8 in long and another is 3 ft 7 in long.
How long are the two planks altogether when laid end to end?

To answer the question we need to add the two lengths together:

ft	in
4	8
+ 3	7
8	3
1	

Adding the inches together gives us 15 inches which is 1 foot 3 inches .... so we put the 3 in the inches column and 'carry' the 1 ft to the ft column.

Answer the following questions:

(a) Ben is 5' 4" tall. His younger brother Ian is 10" shorter.
How tall is Ian?

(b) A box of books is 9" high.
What is the height of six boxes stacked on each other?

(c) The length of a hut is 8 yards, 1 foot , 8 inches and its
width is 5 yards, 2 feet, 3 inches.
Find the perimeter of the hut.

Capacity

2 pints = 1 quart   This can be written: **2 pt = 1 qt**

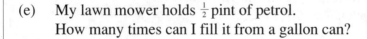
8 pints = 1 gallon .... **8 pt = 1 gall**

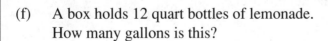
4 quarts = 1 gallon .... **4 qt = 1 gall**

Answer the following questions:

(d) A car petrol tank holds 8 gallons.
How much petrol is left when 2 gallons and 5 pints
have been used?

(e) My lawn mower holds $\frac{1}{2}$ pint of petrol.
How many times can I fill it from a gallon can?

(f) A box holds 12 quart bottles of lemonade.
How many gallons is this?

(g) A fish tank holds 2 gallons and 3 pints of water.
A pet shop has six of these tanks to hold different
types of fish.
How much water was needed to fill the tanks?

Weight

16 ounces = 1 pound   This can be written: 16 oz = 1 lb

14 pounds = 1 stone .... 14 lb = 1 st

8 stone = 1 hundredweight .... 8 st = 1 cwt

20 hundredweight = 1 ton .... 20 cwt = 1 ton

---

Don't forget that **16 ounces make a pound** when you look at the following example:

Six identical parcels each weigh 2 lb 5 oz. Find the total weight.

To answer the question we need to multiply:

lb	oz
2	5
x	6
13	14
1	

Multiplying the 5 ounces by 6 gives us 30 oz. 30 oz is the same as 1 lb 14 oz so we put 14 in the ounces column and carry 1 lb to the pounds column.

The total weight of the six parcels is 13 lb 14 oz.

Answer the following questions:

(a)   Sharon weighs 7 stone and 6 pounds.
How many pounds is this?

(b)   A cake recipe requires 6 oz of sugar. If I make 10 cakes
for the school fete, how much sugar will I need?

(c)   How many pounds are there in one hundredweight?

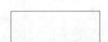

(d)   A bag of sand weighs 1 cwt. If two spadefuls each
weighing 7 lb are taken out, what weight of sand is left?

(e)   I buy $\frac{3}{4}$ lb of cheese. How many ounces is this?

Imperial and Metric Measurements

For each of the main types of measurements we sometimes use imperial units and sometimes metric units. It is useful to be able to roughly convert from one type to the other.

Length

1 metre is a little more than 1 yard.   **2·5 centimetres is a little less than 1 inch.**

8 kilometres is a little less than 5 miles.

So: If a table is **30 inches** high it is approximately 30 x 2·5 cm high. 30 x 2·5 = 75
      The table is approximately **75 cm** high.

      If a chair is 50 cm high it is approximately 50 ÷ 2·5 inches high. 50 ÷ 2·5 = 20
      The chair is approximately 20 inches high.

> **Helpful Hint**
> To divide by 2·5:
> Divide by 5 then
> double your answer.

To change miles to kilometres: Divide by 5 and multiply by 8.
To change kilometres to miles: Divide by 8 and multiply by 5.

Try the following questions. If the answers are not exact round them to the nearest whole number because the answer is only an approximation:

(a)   A greenhouse base measures 9 ft by 6 ft.
      Approximately how long is it in metres?

      Approximately how wide is it in metres?

(b)   A 12 inch ruler is approximately how many cm long?

(c)   My journey to school each day is 15 miles.
      Approximately how many kilometres is this?

(d)   The chimney on top of a three-storey house is 32 ft above
      the ground. Approximately how high is this in metres?

(e)   A picture is 35 cm by 20 cm.
      What is its approximate size in inches?   by

Capacity

1 gallon is a little more than 4·5 litres. 1 litre is a little more than 1·75 pints.

So: If a rain barrel holds 36 gallons of water it holds approximately 36 x 4·5 litres.
36 x 4·5 = 162   The barrel holds approximately 162 litres of water.

If a large bowl holds 7 pints of water it holds approximately 7 ÷ 1·75 litres.
7 ÷ 1·75 = 4   The bowl holds approximately 4 litres of water.

Try the following questions about capacity:

(a)   A two litre lemonade bottle holds approximately
how many pints?

(b)   My car petrol tank holds 47 litres of petrol.
Roughly how many gallons is this?

(c)   A container is filled by pouring 10 quarts
of liquid into it.
How many litre bottles could be filled from the container ?

Weight

1 kilogram is a little more than 2 pounds.   1 pound is a little less than 0·5 kg or 500g.

So: If a cat weighs 6 kg it is approximately 6 x 2 lb. The cat weighs approximately 12 lb.

If a recipe needs $\frac{1}{2}$ lb of flour it needs approximately $\frac{1}{2}$ x 500 g.
The recipe needs approximately 250 g of flour.

Try the following questions about weight:

(d)   I am allowed 20 kg of luggage on my plane trip.
How many pounds is this approximately?

(e)   A recipe needs $\frac{1}{4}$ lb of butter.
Roughly how many grams is this?

(f)   The price of some fish is £2·70 per pound.
What is the approximate price per kilogram?

Symmetry

There are two types of symmetry: **line symmetry** and **rotational symmetry**.

Line symmetry

A line of symmetry can be thought of as a 'fold' line so that if you could fold the paper along the line then one half of the shape would fit exactly on top of itself.

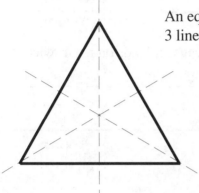

An equilateral triangle has 3 lines of symmetry......

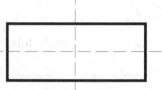

.....and a rectangle has 2 lines of symmetry.

The diagonals of a rectangle are **not** lines of symmetry because one half of the shape would not fold on top of the other half.

How many lines of symmetry has each of the shapes below?

You can draw the lines in if it helps you.

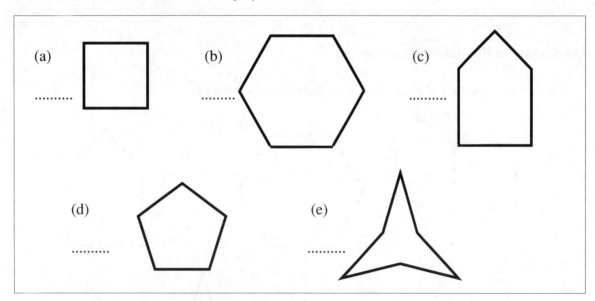

(a) ....

(b) ....

(c) ....

(d) ....

(e) ....

Look at the capital letters below and tick the ones which have lines of symmetry.

The first one has been done for you.

(f) ✓

Rotational symmetry

The order of rotational symmetry tells you **how many times** a shape
will land on top of itself when rotated through 360° about its centre.

This is best seen if one corner is marked:

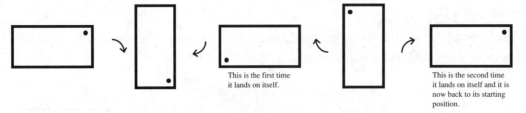

This is the first time
it lands on itself.

This is the second time
it lands on itself and it is
now back to its starting
position.

..... so **a rectangle has rotational symmetry of order 2** because it lands on itself twice.

This is an **irregular** shape.

Although it would land on itself once if rotated
through 360° we actually say that it has no rotational
symmetry because it is **not** a regular shape.

Look again at the shapes from page 41.

Write down the order of rotational symmetry of each shape.

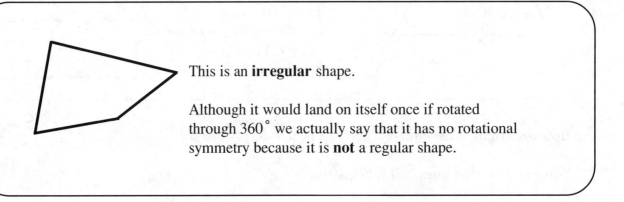

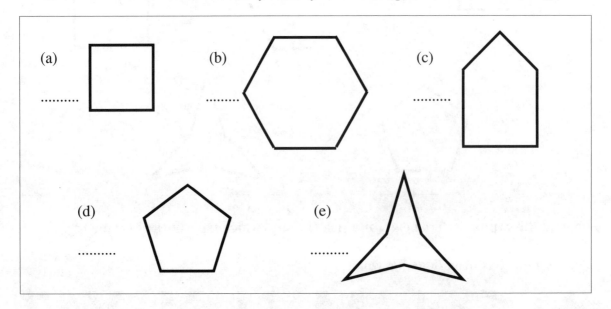

(a) ....

(b) ....

(c) ....

(d) ....

(e) ....

**You may notice a link between the number of lines of symmetry
and the order of rotational symmetry of each shape.**

Fractions of a quantity

A fraction with the numeral **1** on the top is called a **simple fraction**.
To find a simple fraction of a quantity we divide the quantity
by the bottom number of the fraction:

e.g. **Find $\frac{1}{6}$ of 372**

$$6\overline{\smash{)}372}\ \ ^{62}$$

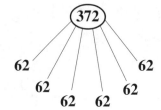

372 can be split into 6 lots of 62

..... so $\frac{1}{6}$ **of 372 is 62**

Find the following fractions of quantities:

(a) $\frac{1}{4}$ of 256

(b) $\frac{1}{3}$ of 174

(c) $\frac{1}{5}$ of 190

(d) $\frac{1}{7}$ of 336

To find a more complicated fraction of a quantity takes two steps.
First, divide by the bottom number then multiply by the top number:

e.g. **Find $\frac{5}{6}$ of 372**

$$6\overline{\smash{)}372}\ \ ^{62} \qquad \begin{array}{r} 62 \\ \times\ 5 \\ \hline 310 \end{array}$$

372 can be split into 6 lots of 62,
we need 5 of these: 5 x 62 = 310

..... so $\frac{5}{6}$ **of 372 is 310**

Find the following fractions of quantities:

(e) $\frac{3}{4}$ of 148

(f) $\frac{2}{3}$ of 258

(g) $\frac{3}{5}$ of 410

(h) $\frac{5}{6}$ of 174

Percentages of a quantity

Percentages are out of a hundred so they measure hundredths of a quantity:

e.g. **Find 16% of 500**

First, find 1% or $\frac{1}{100}$ of 500: $\frac{1}{100}$ of 500 = 5

Then multiply by 16:   16 x 5 = 80

...... so **16% of 500 is 80**

Find the following percentages of quantities:

(a)   12% of 150   [   ]   (b)   4% of 125   [   ]

(c)   15% of 600   [   ]   (d)   80% of 200   [   ]

Some percentages can be done more easily.

Try to remember these: **50% is the same as $\frac{1}{2}$**

25% is the same as $\frac{1}{4}$

75% is the same as $\frac{3}{4}$

10% is the same as $\frac{1}{10}$

10% is perhaps the easiest of all because to find $\frac{1}{10}$ of anything you simply divide by 10. Remember that to divide by 10 you can move the decimal point one place to the left.

Find the following percentages of quantities:

(e)   50% of 736   [   ]   (f)   25% of 800   [   ]

(g)   75% of 400   [   ]   (h)   10% of 14   [   ]

(i)   30% of 40   [   ]   (j)   90% of 90   [   ]

Simple Formulae

A formula is a rule which connects different things in a set way.

For example:

'the maximum number of passengers that can be carried on a coach is four times the number of rows of seats plus one.'

This formula connects the maximum number of passengers to the number of rows of seats.

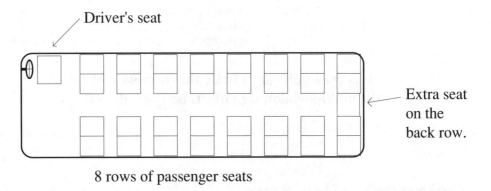

Driver's seat

Extra seat on the back row.

8 rows of passenger seats

So if you know there are eight rows of seats then you can work out that the coach can carry   4 x 8 + 1 = 33 passengers.

Similarly, if you know that a coach can carry 49 passengers then you can work out how many rows there are:

There must be 12 rows because 4 x 12 + 1 = 49.

Using the formula about coach seats try to answer these questions:

(a)   How many passengers can be taken on a coach with 9 rows of seats?

(b)   If a coach can take 29 passengers how many rows of seats has it?

Here is another simple formula:

The perimeter of an equilateral triangle is three times the length of one side.

(c)   Find the perimeter of an equilateral triangle that has sides of length 9 cm.

(d)   If the perimeter of an equilateral triangle is 69 mm
                        what is the length of one side?

Simple Formulae using letters

The questions on page 45 look complicated because of all the words.
They can be made more simple by using letters in place of words.

For example: 'the maximum number of passengers that can be carried on a coach is four times the number of rows of seats plus one.'

This formula can be written like this: P = 4 x R + 1.

Letter **P** represents the number of passengers.

Letter **R** represents the number of rows of seats.

It is even quicker to write the formula without the multiplication sign like this: P = 4R + 1

This still means four times R.

... so, if we know there are 7 rows of seats,
    we can use the formula to find the number of passengers:

P = 4R + 1   →   P = 4 x 7 + 1   →   P = 28 + 1   →   **P = 29**

Using the formula   **P = 4R + 1**   try to answer these questions:

(a)   What is the value of P when R is 10?

(b)   What is the value of R when P is 45?

Look at the other formula from page 45:

The perimeter of an equilateral triangle is three times the length of one side.

.... this formula can be written like this: P = 3L

This time the letter P stands for 'perimeter' and letter L stands for the length of one side.

Using the formula   **P = 3L**   try to answer these questions:

(c)   Find P when L = 14 cm.

(d)   Find L when P = 51 cm.

Organising Data

When information is collected there are several things that can be found in order to understand the information better and perhaps to compare it with similar data.

For example: Ten people were asked their shoe size. The results were:

$$4 , 6 , 4 , 5\frac{1}{2} , 4\frac{1}{2} , 5 , 3 , 4 , 5 , 6\frac{1}{2}$$

First of all it is clearer to write the list in ascending order:

$$3 , 4 , 4 , 4 , 4\frac{1}{2} , 5 , 5 , 5\frac{1}{2} , 6 , 6\frac{1}{2}$$

The **range** shows how far it is from smallest to largest.
In the list above the smallest number is 3 and the biggest is $6\frac{1}{2}$.
The range is therefore **$3\frac{1}{2}$.**

The **mode** is the most common number.
In the list above the mode is **4**.
Sometimes there is no mode.
Sometimes there is more than one mode.

The **median** is the middle number in the list when the numbers are in order.
In the list above there are **two** middle numbers because there is an even number of numbers!
In this case the median is halfway between them.
The two middle numbers in our list are $4\frac{1}{2}$ and 5 so the median is **$4\frac{3}{4}$.**

Use the data provided to answer the following questions:

The temperature was measured at midday every day for a week.
The results were:

$$13° \quad 14° \quad 13° \quad 15° \quad 16° \quad 14° \quad 14°$$

Find the range, mode and median for this data.

(a) range ☐   (b) mode ☐   (c) median ☐

A dozen seeds were planted and one month later their heights were measured.
The heights in mm were:

$$25 \quad 15 \quad 18 \quad 29 \quad 24 \quad 16 \quad 25 \quad 10 \quad 15 \quad 19 \quad 28 \quad 20$$

Find the range, mode and median for this information.

(d) range ☐   (e) mode ☐ & ☐   (f) median ☐

Comparing Data

Sometimes it is useful to compare two or more sets of data.

Look at these two sets of information:

The first seven pupils to get on a school bus had their heights measured to the nearest cm. Their heights were:

$$152 \quad 158 \quad 146 \quad 150 \quad 160 \quad 155 \quad 157$$

The first seven people standing at a town centre bus stop also had their heights measured in cm. Their heights were:

$$152 \quad 173 \quad 181 \quad 149 \quad 180 \quad 174 \quad 181$$

Use the data above to answer the following questions:

(a) Does either set of data above have a mode?
If so, write down what it is and explain your answer:

_____

_____

_____

(b) Write both sets of data in ascending order and find the median for each:

(i) school pupils: _____ median: [   ]

(ii) people at bus stop: _____ median: [   ]

(c) Use the two medians to help you to write a sentence comparing the heights of the two sets of people:

_____

_____

(d) Find the range for each set of data: (i) range: [   ] (ii) range: [   ]

(e) Use the two ranges to help you to write a sentence comparing the spread of heights for the two sets of people:

_____

_____